This
Senior Caregiver
Daily Log Book
Belongs to

_____

_____

Start Date	End Date

Daily Log

Name	Day of the week/Date

Nutrition	
Breakfast	
Snack	
Lunch	
Snack	
Dinner	
Liquids	

Health	
Sleep	
Exercise/Activity	
AM Medications	
PM Medications	
Urine/Bowel Movement	

Hygiene		Notes
Shower/Bath		
Brushed Teeth		
Combed Hair		
Clothes Changed		
Other:		

Daily Log

Name	Day of the week/Date

Nutrition

Breakfast	
Snack	
Lunch	
Snack	
Dinner	
Liquids	

Health

Sleep	
Exercise/Activity	
AM Medications	
PM Medications	
Urine/Bowel Movement	

Hygiene		Notes
Shower/Bath		
Brushed Teeth		
Combed Hair		
Clothes Changed		
Other:		

Daily Log

Name	Day of the week/Date

Nutrition	
Breakfast	
Snack	
Lunch	
Snack	
Dinner	
Liquids	

Health	
Sleep	
Exercise/Activity	
AM Medications	
PM Medications	
Urine/Bowel Movement	

Hygiene		Notes
Shower/Bath		
Brushed Teeth		
Combed Hair		
Clothes Changed		
Other:		

Daily Log

Name	Day of the week/Date

Nutrition	
Breakfast	
Snack	
Lunch	
Snack	
Dinner	
Liquids	

Health	
Sleep	
Exercise/Activity	
AM Medications	
PM Medications	
Urine/Bowel Movement	

Hygiene		Notes
Shower/Bath		
Brushed Teeth		
Combed Hair		
Clothes Changed		
Other:		

Daily Log

Name	Day of the week/Date

Nutrition	
Breakfast	
Snack	
Lunch	
Snack	
Dinner	
Liquids	

Health	
Sleep	
Exercise/Activity	
AM Medications	
PM Medications	
Urine/Bowel Movement	

Hygiene		Notes
Shower/Bath		
Brushed Teeth		
Combed Hair		
Clothes Changed		
Other:		

Daily Log

Name	Day of the week/Date

Nutrition	
Breakfast	
Snack	
Lunch	
Snack	
Dinner	
Liquids	

Health	
Sleep	
Exercise/Activity	
AM Medications	
PM Medications	
Urine/Bowel Movement	

Hygiene		Notes
Shower/Bath		
Brushed Teeth		
Combed Hair		
Clothes Changed		
Other:		

Daily Log

Name	Day of the week/Date

Nutrition	
Breakfast	
Snack	
Lunch	
Snack	
Dinner	
Liquids	

Health	
Sleep	
Exercise/Activity	
AM Medications	
PM Medications	
Urine/Bowel Movement	

Hygiene		Notes
Shower/Bath		
Brushed Teeth		
Combed Hair		
Clothes Changed		
Other:		

Daily Log

Name	Day of the week/Date

Nutrition

Breakfast	
Snack	
Lunch	
Snack	
Dinner	
Liquids	

Health

Sleep	
Exercise/Activity	
AM Medications	
PM Medications	
Urine/Bowel Movement	

Hygiene		Notes
Shower/Bath		
Brushed Teeth		
Combed Hair		
Clothes Changed		
Other:		

Daily Log

Name	Day of the week/Date

Nutrition

Breakfast	
Snack	
Lunch	
Snack	
Dinner	
Liquids	

Health

Sleep	
Exercise/Activity	
AM Medications	
PM Medications	
Urine/Bowel Movement	

Hygiene		Notes
Shower/Bath		
Brushed Teeth		
Combed Hair		
Clothes Changed		
Other:		

Daily Log

Name	Day of the week/Date

Nutrition	
Breakfast	
Snack	
Lunch	
Snack	
Dinner	
Liquids	

Health	
Sleep	
Exercise/Activity	
AM Medications	
PM Medications	
Urine/Bowel Movement	

Hygiene		Notes
Shower/Bath		
Brushed Teeth		
Combed Hair		
Clothes Changed		
Other:		

_____

_____

_____

_____

Daily Log

Name	Day of the week/Date

Nutrition	
Breakfast	
Snack	
Lunch	
Snack	
Dinner	
Liquids	

Health	
Sleep	
Exercise/Activity	
AM Medications	
PM Medications	
Urine/Bowel Movement	

Hygiene		Notes
Shower/Bath		
Brushed Teeth		
Combed Hair		
Clothes Changed		
Other:		

Daily Log

Name	Day of the week/Date

Nutrition	
Breakfast	
Snack	
Lunch	
Snack	
Dinner	
Liquids	

Health	
Sleep	
Exercise/Activity	
AM Medications	
PM Medications	
Urine/Bowel Movement	

Hygiene		Notes
Shower/Bath		
Brushed Teeth		
Combed Hair		
Clothes Changed		
Other:		

Daily Log

Name	Day of the week/Date

Nutrition

Breakfast	
Snack	
Lunch	
Snack	
Dinner	
Liquids	

Health

Sleep	
Exercise/Activity	
AM Medications	
PM Medications	
Urine/Bowel Movement	

Hygiene		Notes
Shower/Bath		
Brushed Teeth		
Combed Hair		
Clothes Changed		
Other:		

Daily Log

Name	Day of the week/Date

Nutrition	
Breakfast	
Snack	
Lunch	
Snack	
Dinner	
Liquids	

Health	
Sleep	
Exercise/Activity	
AM Medications	
PM Medications	
Urine/Bowel Movement	

Hygiene		Notes
Shower/Bath		
Brushed Teeth		
Combed Hair		
Clothes Changed		
Other:		

Daily Log

Name	Day of the week/Date

Nutrition	
Breakfast	
Snack	
Lunch	
Snack	
Dinner	
Liquids	

Health	
Sleep	
Exercise/Activity	
AM Medications	
PM Medications	
Urine/Bowel Movement	

Hygiene		Notes
Shower/Bath		
Brushed Teeth		
Combed Hair		
Clothes Changed		
Other:		

Daily Log

Name	Day of the week/Date

Nutrition	
Breakfast	
Snack	
Lunch	
Snack	
Dinner	
Liquids	

Health	
Sleep	
Exercise/Activity	
AM Medications	
PM Medications	
Urine/Bowel Movement	

Hygiene		Notes
Shower/Bath		
Brushed Teeth		
Combed Hair		
Clothes Changed		
Other:		

Daily Log

Name	Day of the week/Date

Nutrition	
Breakfast	
Snack	
Lunch	
Snack	
Dinner	
Liquids	

Health	
Sleep	
Exercise/Activity	
AM Medications	
PM Medications	
Urine/Bowel Movement	

Hygiene		Notes
Shower/Bath		
Brushed Teeth		
Combed Hair		
Clothes Changed		
Other:		

Daily Log

Name	Day of the week/Date

Nutrition	
Breakfast	
Snack	
Lunch	
Snack	
Dinner	
Liquids	

Health	
Sleep	
Exercise/Activity	
AM Medications	
PM Medications	
Urine/Bowel Movement	

Hygiene		Notes
Shower/Bath		
Brushed Teeth		
Combed Hair		
Clothes Changed		
Other:		

Daily Log

Name	Day of the week/Date

Nutrition	
Breakfast	
Snack	
Lunch	
Snack	
Dinner	
Liquids	

Health	
Sleep	
Exercise/Activity	
AM Medications	
PM Medications	
Urine/Bowel Movement	

Hygiene		Notes
Shower/Bath		
Brushed Teeth		
Combed Hair		
Clothes Changed		
Other:		

Daily Log

Name	Day of the week/Date

Nutrition	
Breakfast	
Snack	
Lunch	
Snack	
Dinner	
Liquids	

Health	
Sleep	
Exercise/Activity	
AM Medications	
PM Medications	
Urine/Bowel Movement	

Hygiene		Notes
Shower/Bath		
Brushed Teeth		
Combed Hair		
Clothes Changed		
Other:		

Daily Log

Name	Day of the week/Date

Nutrition	
Breakfast	
Snack	
Lunch	
Snack	
Dinner	
Liquids	

Health	
Sleep	
Exercise/Activity	
AM Medications	
PM Medications	
Urine/Bowel Movement	

Hygiene		Notes
Shower/Bath		
Brushed Teeth		
Combed Hair		
Clothes Changed		
Other:		

Daily Log

Name	Day of the week/Date

Nutrition	
Breakfast	
Snack	
Lunch	
Snack	
Dinner	
Liquids	

Health	
Sleep	
Exercise/Activity	
AM Medications	
PM Medications	
Urine/Bowel Movement	

Hygiene		Notes
Shower/Bath		
Brushed Teeth		
Combed Hair		
Clothes Changed		
Other:		

Daily Log

Name	Day of the week/Date

Nutrition

Breakfast	
Snack	
Lunch	
Snack	
Dinner	
Liquids	

Health

Sleep	
Exercise/Activity	
AM Medications	
PM Medications	
Urine/Bowel Movement	

Hygiene		Notes
Shower/Bath		
Brushed Teeth		
Combed Hair		
Clothes Changed		
Other:		

Daily Log

Name	Day of the week/Date

Nutrition

Breakfast	
Snack	
Lunch	
Snack	
Dinner	
Liquids	

Health

Sleep	
Exercise/Activity	
AM Medications	
PM Medications	
Urine/Bowel Movement	

Hygiene		Notes
Shower/Bath		
Brushed Teeth		
Combed Hair		
Clothes Changed		
Other:		

Daily Log

Name	Day of the week/Date

Nutrition

Breakfast	
Snack	
Lunch	
Snack	
Dinner	
Liquids	

Health

Sleep	
Exercise/Activity	
AM Medications	
PM Medications	
Urine/Bowel Movement	

Hygiene		Notes
Shower/Bath		
Brushed Teeth		
Combed Hair		
Clothes Changed		
Other:		

Daily Log

Name	Day of the week/Date

Nutrition	
Breakfast	
Snack	
Lunch	
Snack	
Dinner	
Liquids	

Health	
Sleep	
Exercise/Activity	
AM Medications	
PM Medications	
Urine/Bowel Movement	

Hygiene		Notes
Shower/Bath		
Brushed Teeth		
Combed Hair		
Clothes Changed		
Other:		

Daily Log

Name	Day of the week/Date

Nutrition

Breakfast	
Snack	
Lunch	
Snack	
Dinner	
Liquids	

Health

Sleep	
Exercise/Activity	
AM Medications	
PM Medications	
Urine/Bowel Movement	

Hygiene		Notes
Shower/Bath		
Brushed Teeth		
Combed Hair		
Clothes Changed		
Other:		

Daily Log

Name	Day of the week/Date

Nutrition	
Breakfast	
Snack	
Lunch	
Snack	
Dinner	
Liquids	

Health	
Sleep	
Exercise/Activity	
AM Medications	
PM Medications	
Urine/Bowel Movement	

Hygiene		Notes
Shower/Bath		
Brushed Teeth		
Combed Hair		
Clothes Changed		
Other:		

Daily Log

Name	Day of the week/Date

Nutrition	
Breakfast	
Snack	
Lunch	
Snack	
Dinner	
Liquids	

Health	
Sleep	
Exercise/Activity	
AM Medications	
PM Medications	
Urine/Bowel Movement	

Hygiene		Notes
Shower/Bath		
Brushed Teeth		
Combed Hair		
Clothes Changed		
Other:		

Daily Log

Name	Day of the week/Date

Nutrition	
Breakfast	
Snack	
Lunch	
Snack	
Dinner	
Liquids	

Health	
Sleep	
Exercise/Activity	
AM Medications	
PM Medications	
Urine/Bowel Movement	

Hygiene		Notes
Shower/Bath		
Brushed Teeth		
Combed Hair		
Clothes Changed		
Other:		

Daily Log

Name	Day of the week/Date

Nutrition	
Breakfast	
Snack	
Lunch	
Snack	
Dinner	
Liquids	

Health	
Sleep	
Exercise/Activity	
AM Medications	
PM Medications	
Urine/Bowel Movement	

Hygiene		Notes
Shower/Bath		
Brushed Teeth		
Combed Hair		
Clothes Changed		
Other:		

Daily Log

Name	Day of the week/Date

Nutrition	
Breakfast	
Snack	
Lunch	
Snack	
Dinner	
Liquids	

Health	
Sleep	
Exercise/Activity	
AM Medications	
PM Medications	
Urine/Bowel Movement	

Hygiene		Notes
Shower/Bath		
Brushed Teeth		
Combed Hair		
Clothes Changed		
Other:		

Daily Log

Name	Day of the week/Date

Nutrition	
Breakfast	
Snack	
Lunch	
Snack	
Dinner	
Liquids	

Health	
Sleep	
Exercise/Activity	
AM Medications	
PM Medications	
Urine/Bowel Movement	

Hygiene		Notes
Shower/Bath		
Brushed Teeth		
Combed Hair		
Clothes Changed		
Other:		

Daily Log

Name	Day of the week/Date

Nutrition	
Breakfast	
Snack	
Lunch	
Snack	
Dinner	
Liquids	

Health	
Sleep	
Exercise/Activity	
AM Medications	
PM Medications	
Urine/Bowel Movement	

Hygiene		Notes
Shower/Bath		
Brushed Teeth		
Combed Hair		
Clothes Changed		
Other:		

Daily Log

Name	Day of the week/Date

Nutrition	
Breakfast	
Snack	
Lunch	
Snack	
Dinner	
Liquids	

Health	
Sleep	
Exercise/Activity	
AM Medications	
PM Medications	
Urine/Bowel Movement	

Hygiene		Notes
Shower/Bath		
Brushed Teeth		
Combed Hair		
Clothes Changed		
Other:		

Daily Log

Name	Day of the week/Date

Nutrition	
Breakfast	
Snack	
Lunch	
Snack	
Dinner	
Liquids	

Health	
Sleep	
Exercise/Activity	
AM Medications	
PM Medications	
Urine/Bowel Movement	

Hygiene		Notes
Shower/Bath		
Brushed Teeth		
Combed Hair		
Clothes Changed		
Other:		

Daily Log

Name	Day of the week/Date

Nutrition	
Breakfast	
Snack	
Lunch	
Snack	
Dinner	
Liquids	

Health	
Sleep	
Exercise/Activity	
AM Medications	
PM Medications	
Urine/Bowel Movement	

Hygiene		Notes
Shower/Bath		
Brushed Teeth		
Combed Hair		
Clothes Changed		
Other:		

Daily Log

Name	Day of the week/Date

Nutrition	
Breakfast	
Snack	
Lunch	
Snack	
Dinner	
Liquids	

Health	
Sleep	
Exercise/Activity	
AM Medications	
PM Medications	
Urine/Bowel Movement	

Hygiene		Notes
Shower/Bath		
Brushed Teeth		
Combed Hair		
Clothes Changed		
Other:		

Daily Log

Name	Day of the week/Date

Nutrition	
Breakfast	
Snack	
Lunch	
Snack	
Dinner	
Liquids	

Health	
Sleep	
Exercise/Activity	
AM Medications	
PM Medications	
Urine/Bowel Movement	

Hygiene		Notes
Shower/Bath		
Brushed Teeth		
Combed Hair		
Clothes Changed		
Other:		

Daily Log

Name	Day of the week/Date

Nutrition	
Breakfast	
Snack	
Lunch	
Snack	
Dinner	
Liquids	

Health	
Sleep	
Exercise/Activity	
AM Medications	
PM Medications	
Urine/Bowel Movement	

Hygiene		Notes
Shower/Bath		
Brushed Teeth		
Combed Hair		
Clothes Changed		
Other:		

Daily Log

Name	Day of the week/Date

Nutrition	
Breakfast	
Snack	
Lunch	
Snack	
Dinner	
Liquids	

Health	
Sleep	
Exercise/Activity	
AM Medications	
PM Medications	
Urine/Bowel Movement	

Hygiene		Notes
Shower/Bath		
Brushed Teeth		
Combed Hair		
Clothes Changed		
Other:		

Daily Log

Name	Day of the week/Date

Nutrition

Breakfast	
Snack	
Lunch	
Snack	
Dinner	
Liquids	

Health

Sleep	
Exercise/Activity	
AM Medications	
PM Medications	
Urine/Bowel Movement	

Hygiene		Notes
Shower/Bath		
Brushed Teeth		
Combed Hair		
Clothes Changed		
Other:		

Daily Log

Name	Day of the week/Date

Nutrition	
Breakfast	
Snack	
Lunch	
Snack	
Dinner	
Liquids	

Health	
Sleep	
Exercise/Activity	
AM Medications	
PM Medications	
Urine/Bowel Movement	

Hygiene		Notes
Shower/Bath		
Brushed Teeth		
Combed Hair		
Clothes Changed		
Other:		

Daily Log

Name	Day of the week/Date

Nutrition	
Breakfast	
Snack	
Lunch	
Snack	
Dinner	
Liquids	

Health	
Sleep	
Exercise/Activity	
AM Medications	
PM Medications	
Urine/Bowel Movement	

Hygiene		Notes
Shower/Bath		
Brushed Teeth		
Combed Hair		
Clothes Changed		
Other:		

Daily Log

Name	Day of the week/Date

Nutrition	
Breakfast	
Snack	
Lunch	
Snack	
Dinner	
Liquids	

Health	
Sleep	
Exercise/Activity	
AM Medications	
PM Medications	
Urine/Bowel Movement	

Hygiene		Notes
Shower/Bath		
Brushed Teeth		
Combed Hair		
Clothes Changed		
Other:		

Daily Log

Name	Day of the week/Date

Nutrition	
Breakfast	
Snack	
Lunch	
Snack	
Dinner	
Liquids	

Health	
Sleep	
Exercise/Activity	
AM Medications	
PM Medications	
Urine/Bowel Movement	

Hygiene		Notes
Shower/Bath		
Brushed Teeth		
Combed Hair		
Clothes Changed		
Other:		

Daily Log

Name	Day of the week/Date

Nutrition

Breakfast	
Snack	
Lunch	
Snack	
Dinner	
Liquids	

Health

Sleep	
Exercise/Activity	
AM Medications	
PM Medications	
Urine/Bowel Movement	

Hygiene		Notes
Shower/Bath		
Brushed Teeth		
Combed Hair		
Clothes Changed		
Other:		

Daily Log

Name	Day of the week/Date

Nutrition	
Breakfast	
Snack	
Lunch	
Snack	
Dinner	
Liquids	

Health	
Sleep	
Exercise/Activity	
AM Medications	
PM Medications	
Urine/Bowel Movement	

Hygiene		Notes
Shower/Bath		
Brushed Teeth		
Combed Hair		
Clothes Changed		
Other:		

Daily Log

Name	Day of the week/Date

Nutrition	
Breakfast	
Snack	
Lunch	
Snack	
Dinner	
Liquids	

Health	
Sleep	
Exercise/Activity	
AM Medications	
PM Medications	
Urine/Bowel Movement	

Hygiene		Notes
Shower/Bath		
Brushed Teeth		
Combed Hair		
Clothes Changed		
Other:		

Daily Log

Name	Day of the week/Date

Nutrition	
Breakfast	
Snack	
Lunch	
Snack	
Dinner	
Liquids	

Health	
Sleep	
Exercise/Activity	
AM Medications	
PM Medications	
Urine/Bowel Movement	

Hygiene		Notes
Shower/Bath		
Brushed Teeth		
Combed Hair		
Clothes Changed		
Other:		

Daily Log

Name	Day of the week/Date

Nutrition	
Breakfast	
Snack	
Lunch	
Snack	
Dinner	
Liquids	

Health	
Sleep	
Exercise/Activity	
AM Medications	
PM Medications	
Urine/Bowel Movement	

Hygiene		Notes
Shower/Bath		
Brushed Teeth		
Combed Hair		
Clothes Changed		
Other:		

Daily Log

Name	Day of the week/Date

Nutrition	
Breakfast	
Snack	
Lunch	
Snack	
Dinner	
Liquids	

Health	
Sleep	
Exercise/Activity	
AM Medications	
PM Medications	
Urine/Bowel Movement	

Hygiene		Notes
Shower/Bath		
Brushed Teeth		
Combed Hair		
Clothes Changed		
Other:		

Daily Log

Name	Day of the week/Date

Nutrition	
Breakfast	
Snack	
Lunch	
Snack	
Dinner	
Liquids	

Health	
Sleep	
Exercise/Activity	
AM Medications	
PM Medications	
Urine/Bowel Movement	

Hygiene		Notes
Shower/Bath		
Brushed Teeth		
Combed Hair		
Clothes Changed		
Other:		

Daily Log

Name	Day of the week/Date

Nutrition	
Breakfast	
Snack	
Lunch	
Snack	
Dinner	
Liquids	

Health	
Sleep	
Exercise/Activity	
AM Medications	
PM Medications	
Urine/Bowel Movement	

Hygiene		Notes
Shower/Bath		
Brushed Teeth		
Combed Hair		
Clothes Changed		
Other:		

Daily Log

Name	Day of the week/Date

Nutrition

Breakfast	
Snack	
Lunch	
Snack	
Dinner	
Liquids	

Health

Sleep	
Exercise/Activity	
AM Medications	
PM Medications	
Urine/Bowel Movement	

Hygiene		Notes
Shower/Bath		
Brushed Teeth		
Combed Hair		
Clothes Changed		
Other:		

Daily Log

Name	Day of the week/Date

Nutrition	
Breakfast	
Snack	
Lunch	
Snack	
Dinner	
Liquids	

Health	
Sleep	
Exercise/Activity	
AM Medications	
PM Medications	
Urine/Bowel Movement	

Hygiene	
Shower/Bath	
Brushed Teeth	
Combed Hair	
Clothes Changed	
Other:	

Notes

_____

_____

_____

_____

_____

_____

_____

_____

_____

Daily Log

Name	Day of the week/Date

Nutrition	
Breakfast	
Snack	
Lunch	
Snack	
Dinner	
Liquids	

Health	
Sleep	
Exercise/Activity	
AM Medications	
PM Medications	
Urine/Bowel Movement	

Hygiene		Notes
Shower/Bath		
Brushed Teeth		
Combed Hair		
Clothes Changed		
Other:		

Daily Log

Name	Day of the week/Date

Nutrition	
Breakfast	
Snack	
Lunch	
Snack	
Dinner	
Liquids	

Health	
Sleep	
Exercise/Activity	
AM Medications	
PM Medications	
Urine/Bowel Movement	

Hygiene		Notes
Shower/Bath		
Brushed Teeth		
Combed Hair		
Clothes Changed		
Other:		

Daily Log

Name	Day of the week/Date

Nutrition	
Breakfast	
Snack	
Lunch	
Snack	
Dinner	
Liquids	

Health	
Sleep	
Exercise/Activity	
AM Medications	
PM Medications	
Urine/Bowel Movement	

Hygiene		Notes
Shower/Bath		
Brushed Teeth		
Combed Hair		
Clothes Changed		
Other:		

Daily Log

Name	Day of the week/Date

Nutrition	
Breakfast	
Snack	
Lunch	
Snack	
Dinner	
Liquids	

Health	
Sleep	
Exercise/Activity	
AM Medications	
PM Medications	
Urine/Bowel Movement	

Hygiene	
Shower/Bath	
Brushed Teeth	
Combed Hair	
Clothes Changed	
Other:	

Notes

Daily Log

Name	Day of the week/Date

Nutrition	
Breakfast	
Snack	
Lunch	
Snack	
Dinner	
Liquids	

Health	
Sleep	
Exercise/Activity	
AM Medications	
PM Medications	
Urine/Bowel Movement	

Hygiene		Notes
Shower/Bath		
Brushed Teeth		
Combed Hair		
Clothes Changed		
Other:		

Daily Log

Name	Day of the week/Date

Nutrition	
Breakfast	
Snack	
Lunch	
Snack	
Dinner	
Liquids	

Health	
Sleep	
Exercise/Activity	
AM Medications	
PM Medications	
Urine/Bowel Movement	

Hygiene	
Shower/Bath	
Brushed Teeth	
Combed Hair	
Clothes Changed	
Other:	

Notes

_____
_____
_____
_____
_____

_____
_____
_____
_____

Daily Log

Name	Day of the week/Date

Nutrition	
Breakfast	
Snack	
Lunch	
Snack	
Dinner	
Liquids	

Health	
Sleep	
Exercise/Activity	
AM Medications	
PM Medications	
Urine/Bowel Movement	

Hygiene		Notes
Shower/Bath		
Brushed Teeth		
Combed Hair		
Clothes Changed		
Other:		

Daily Log

Name	Day of the week/Date

Nutrition	
Breakfast	
Snack	
Lunch	
Snack	
Dinner	
Liquids	

Health	
Sleep	
Exercise/Activity	
AM Medications	
PM Medications	
Urine/Bowel Movement	

Hygiene		Notes
Shower/Bath		
Brushed Teeth		
Combed Hair		
Clothes Changed		
Other:		

Daily Log

Name	Day of the week/Date

Nutrition

Breakfast	
Snack	
Lunch	
Snack	
Dinner	
Liquids	

Health

Sleep	
Exercise/Activity	
AM Medications	
PM Medications	
Urine/Bowel Movement	

Hygiene		Notes
Shower/Bath		
Brushed Teeth		
Combed Hair		
Clothes Changed		
Other:		

Daily Log

Name	Day of the week/Date

Nutrition

Breakfast	
Snack	
Lunch	
Snack	
Dinner	
Liquids	

Health

Sleep	
Exercise/Activity	
AM Medications	
PM Medications	
Urine/Bowel Movement	

Hygiene		Notes
Shower/Bath		_____
Brushed Teeth		_____
Combed Hair		_____
Clothes Changed		_____
Other:		_____

_____

_____

_____

_____

_____

Daily Log

Name	Day of the week/Date

Nutrition	
Breakfast	
Snack	
Lunch	
Snack	
Dinner	
Liquids	

Health	
Sleep	
Exercise/Activity	
AM Medications	
PM Medications	
Urine/Bowel Movement	

Hygiene		Notes
Shower/Bath		
Brushed Teeth		
Combed Hair		
Clothes Changed		
Other:		

Daily Log

Name	Day of the week/Date

Nutrition	
Breakfast	
Snack	
Lunch	
Snack	
Dinner	
Liquids	

Health	
Sleep	
Exercise/Activity	
AM Medications	
PM Medications	
Urine/Bowel Movement	

Hygiene	
Shower/Bath	
Brushed Teeth	
Combed Hair	
Clothes Changed	
Other:	

Notes

_____

_____

_____

_____

_____

_____

_____

_____

_____

Daily Log

Name	Day of the week/Date

Nutrition	
Breakfast	
Snack	
Lunch	
Snack	
Dinner	
Liquids	

Health	
Sleep	
Exercise/Activity	
AM Medications	
PM Medications	
Urine/Bowel Movement	

Hygiene		Notes
Shower/Bath		
Brushed Teeth		
Combed Hair		
Clothes Changed		
Other:		

Daily Log

Name	Day of the week/Date

Nutrition

Breakfast	
Snack	
Lunch	
Snack	
Dinner	
Liquids	

Health

Sleep	
Exercise/Activity	
AM Medications	
PM Medications	
Urine/Bowel Movement	

Hygiene		Notes
Shower/Bath		
Brushed Teeth		
Combed Hair		
Clothes Changed		
Other:		

Daily Log

Name	Day of the week/Date

Nutrition

Breakfast	
Snack	
Lunch	
Snack	
Dinner	
Liquids	

Health

Sleep	
Exercise/Activity	
AM Medications	
PM Medications	
Urine/Bowel Movement	

Hygiene		Notes
Shower/Bath		
Brushed Teeth		
Combed Hair		
Clothes Changed		
Other:		

Daily Log

Name	Day of the week/Date

Nutrition	
Breakfast	
Snack	
Lunch	
Snack	
Dinner	
Liquids	

Health	
Sleep	
Exercise/Activity	
AM Medications	
PM Medications	
Urine/Bowel Movement	

Hygiene	
Shower/Bath	
Brushed Teeth	
Combed Hair	
Clothes Changed	
Other:	

Notes

_____

_____

_____

_____

_____

_____

_____

_____

_____

_____

Daily Log

Name	Day of the week/Date

Nutrition	
Breakfast	
Snack	
Lunch	
Snack	
Dinner	
Liquids	

Health	
Sleep	
Exercise/Activity	
AM Medications	
PM Medications	
Urine/Bowel Movement	

Hygiene		Notes
Shower/Bath		
Brushed Teeth		
Combed Hair		
Clothes Changed		
Other:		

Daily Log

Name	Day of the week/Date

Nutrition	
Breakfast	
Snack	
Lunch	
Snack	
Dinner	
Liquids	

Health	
Sleep	
Exercise/Activity	
AM Medications	
PM Medications	
Urine/Bowel Movement	

Hygiene	
Shower/Bath	
Brushed Teeth	
Combed Hair	
Clothes Changed	
Other:	

Notes

_____
_____
_____
_____
_____

_____
_____
_____
_____

Daily Log

Name	Day of the week/Date

Nutrition

Breakfast	
Snack	
Lunch	
Snack	
Dinner	
Liquids	

Health

Sleep	
Exercise/Activity	
AM Medications	
PM Medications	
Urine/Bowel Movement	

Hygiene		Notes
Shower/Bath		
Brushed Teeth		
Combed Hair		
Clothes Changed		
Other:		

Daily Log

Name	Day of the week/Date

Nutrition	
Breakfast	
Snack	
Lunch	
Snack	
Dinner	
Liquids	

Health	
Sleep	
Exercise/Activity	
AM Medications	
PM Medications	
Urine/Bowel Movement	

Hygiene		Notes
Shower/Bath		
Brushed Teeth		
Combed Hair		
Clothes Changed		
Other:		

Daily Log

Name	Day of the week/Date

Nutrition	
Breakfast	
Snack	
Lunch	
Snack	
Dinner	
Liquids	

Health	
Sleep	
Exercise/Activity	
AM Medications	
PM Medications	
Urine/Bowel Movement	

Hygiene		Notes
Shower/Bath		
Brushed Teeth		
Combed Hair		
Clothes Changed		
Other:		

Daily Log

Name	Day of the week/Date

Nutrition	
Breakfast	
Snack	
Lunch	
Snack	
Dinner	
Liquids	

Health	
Sleep	
Exercise/Activity	
AM Medications	
PM Medications	
Urine/Bowel Movement	

Hygiene	
Shower/Bath	
Brushed Teeth	
Combed Hair	
Clothes Changed	
Other:	

Notes

Daily Log

Name	Day of the week/Date

Nutrition	
Breakfast	
Snack	
Lunch	
Snack	
Dinner	
Liquids	

Health	
Sleep	
Exercise/Activity	
AM Medications	
PM Medications	
Urine/Bowel Movement	

Hygiene		Notes
Shower/Bath		
Brushed Teeth		
Combed Hair		
Clothes Changed		
Other:		

Daily Log

Name	Day of the week/Date

Nutrition

Breakfast	
Snack	
Lunch	
Snack	
Dinner	
Liquids	

Health

Sleep	
Exercise/Activity	
AM Medications	
PM Medications	
Urine/Bowel Movement	

Hygiene		Notes
Shower/Bath		
Brushed Teeth		
Combed Hair		
Clothes Changed		
Other:		

Daily Log

Name	Day of the week/Date

Nutrition	
Breakfast	
Snack	
Lunch	
Snack	
Dinner	
Liquids	

Health	
Sleep	
Exercise/Activity	
AM Medications	
PM Medications	
Urine/Bowel Movement	

Hygiene		Notes
Shower/Bath		
Brushed Teeth		
Combed Hair		
Clothes Changed		
Other:		

Daily Log

Name	Day of the week/Date

Nutrition	
Breakfast	
Snack	
Lunch	
Snack	
Dinner	
Liquids	

Health	
Sleep	
Exercise/Activity	
AM Medications	
PM Medications	
Urine/Bowel Movement	

Hygiene		Notes
Shower/Bath		
Brushed Teeth		
Combed Hair		
Clothes Changed		
Other:		

Daily Log

Name	Day of the week/Date

Nutrition

Breakfast	
Snack	
Lunch	
Snack	
Dinner	
Liquids	

Health

Sleep	
Exercise/Activity	
AM Medications	
PM Medications	
Urine/Bowel Movement	

Hygiene		Notes
Shower/Bath		
Brushed Teeth		
Combed Hair		
Clothes Changed		
Other:		

Daily Log

Name	Day of the week/Date

Nutrition	
Breakfast	
Snack	
Lunch	
Snack	
Dinner	
Liquids	

Health	
Sleep	
Exercise/Activity	
AM Medications	
PM Medications	
Urine/Bowel Movement	

Hygiene		Notes
Shower/Bath		
Brushed Teeth		
Combed Hair		
Clothes Changed		
Other:		

Daily Log

Name	Day of the week/Date

Nutrition	
Breakfast	
Snack	
Lunch	
Snack	
Dinner	
Liquids	

Health	
Sleep	
Exercise/Activity	
AM Medications	
PM Medications	
Urine/Bowel Movement	

Hygiene		Notes
Shower/Bath		
Brushed Teeth		
Combed Hair		
Clothes Changed		
Other:		

Daily Log

Name	Day of the week/Date

Nutrition	
Breakfast	
Snack	
Lunch	
Snack	
Dinner	
Liquids	

Health	
Sleep	
Exercise/Activity	
AM Medications	
PM Medications	
Urine/Bowel Movement	

Hygiene		Notes
Shower/Bath		
Brushed Teeth		
Combed Hair		
Clothes Changed		
Other:		

Daily Log

Name	Day of the week/Date

Nutrition

Breakfast	
Snack	
Lunch	
Snack	
Dinner	
Liquids	

Health

Sleep	
Exercise/Activity	
AM Medications	
PM Medications	
Urine/Bowel Movement	

Hygiene		Notes
Shower/Bath		
Brushed Teeth		
Combed Hair		
Clothes Changed		
Other:		

Daily Log

Name	Day of the week/Date

Nutrition	
Breakfast	
Snack	
Lunch	
Snack	
Dinner	
Liquids	

Health	
Sleep	
Exercise/Activity	
AM Medications	
PM Medications	
Urine/Bowel Movement	

Hygiene		Notes
Shower/Bath		
Brushed Teeth		
Combed Hair		
Clothes Changed		
Other:		

Daily Log

Name	Day of the week/Date

Nutrition	
Breakfast	
Snack	
Lunch	
Snack	
Dinner	
Liquids	

Health	
Sleep	
Exercise/Activity	
AM Medications	
PM Medications	
Urine/Bowel Movement	

Hygiene		Notes
Shower/Bath		
Brushed Teeth		
Combed Hair		
Clothes Changed		
Other:		

Daily Log

Name	Day of the week/Date

Nutrition	
Breakfast	
Snack	
Lunch	
Snack	
Dinner	
Liquids	

Health	
Sleep	
Exercise/Activity	
AM Medications	
PM Medications	
Urine/Bowel Movement	

Hygiene		Notes
Shower/Bath		
Brushed Teeth		
Combed Hair		
Clothes Changed		
Other:		

Daily Log

Name	Day of the week/Date

Nutrition

Breakfast	
Snack	
Lunch	
Snack	
Dinner	
Liquids	

Health

Sleep	
Exercise/Activity	
AM Medications	
PM Medications	
Urine/Bowel Movement	

Hygiene		Notes
Shower/Bath		
Brushed Teeth		
Combed Hair		
Clothes Changed		
Other:		

Daily Log

Name	Day of the week/Date

Nutrition	
Breakfast	
Snack	
Lunch	
Snack	
Dinner	
Liquids	

Health	
Sleep	
Exercise/Activity	
AM Medications	
PM Medications	
Urine/Bowel Movement	

Hygiene		Notes
Shower/Bath		
Brushed Teeth		
Combed Hair		
Clothes Changed		
Other:		

Daily Log

Name	Day of the week/Date

Nutrition	
Breakfast	
Snack	
Lunch	
Snack	
Dinner	
Liquids	

Health	
Sleep	
Exercise/Activity	
AM Medications	
PM Medications	
Urine/Bowel Movement	

Hygiene		Notes
Shower/Bath		
Brushed Teeth		
Combed Hair		
Clothes Changed		
Other:		

Daily Log

Name	Day of the week/Date

Nutrition	
Breakfast	
Snack	
Lunch	
Snack	
Dinner	
Liquids	

Health	
Sleep	
Exercise/Activity	
AM Medications	
PM Medications	
Urine/Bowel Movement	

Hygiene		Notes
Shower/Bath		
Brushed Teeth		
Combed Hair		
Clothes Changed		
Other:		

Daily Log

Name	Day of the week/Date

Nutrition	
Breakfast	
Snack	
Lunch	
Snack	
Dinner	
Liquids	

Health	
Sleep	
Exercise/Activity	
AM Medications	
PM Medications	
Urine/Bowel Movement	

Hygiene		Notes
Shower/Bath		
Brushed Teeth		
Combed Hair		
Clothes Changed		
Other:		

Daily Log

Name	Day of the week/Date

Nutrition	
Breakfast	
Snack	
Lunch	
Snack	
Dinner	
Liquids	

Health	
Sleep	
Exercise/Activity	
AM Medications	
PM Medications	
Urine/Bowel Movement	

Hygiene		Notes
Shower/Bath		
Brushed Teeth		
Combed Hair		
Clothes Changed		
Other:		

Daily Log

Name	Day of the week/Date

Nutrition	
Breakfast	
Snack	
Lunch	
Snack	
Dinner	
Liquids	

Health	
Sleep	
Exercise/Activity	
AM Medications	
PM Medications	
Urine/Bowel Movement	

Hygiene		Notes
Shower/Bath		
Brushed Teeth		
Combed Hair		
Clothes Changed		
Other:		

Daily Log

Name	Day of the week/Date

Nutrition	
Breakfast	
Snack	
Lunch	
Snack	
Dinner	
Liquids	

Health	
Sleep	
Exercise/Activity	
AM Medications	
PM Medications	
Urine/Bowel Movement	

Hygiene		Notes
Shower/Bath		
Brushed Teeth		
Combed Hair		
Clothes Changed		
Other:		

Daily Log

Name	Day of the week/Date

Nutrition

Breakfast	
Snack	
Lunch	
Snack	
Dinner	
Liquids	

Health

Sleep	
Exercise/Activity	
AM Medications	
PM Medications	
Urine/Bowel Movement	

Hygiene		Notes
Shower/Bath		
Brushed Teeth		
Combed Hair		
Clothes Changed		
Other:		

Daily Log

Name	Day of the week/Date

Nutrition	
Breakfast	
Snack	
Lunch	
Snack	
Dinner	
Liquids	

Health	
Sleep	
Exercise/Activity	
AM Medications	
PM Medications	
Urine/Bowel Movement	

Hygiene		Notes
Shower/Bath		
Brushed Teeth		
Combed Hair		
Clothes Changed		
Other:		

Daily Log

Name	Day of the week/Date

Nutrition	
Breakfast	
Snack	
Lunch	
Snack	
Dinner	
Liquids	

Health	
Sleep	
Exercise/Activity	
AM Medications	
PM Medications	
Urine/Bowel Movement	

Hygiene		Notes
Shower/Bath		
Brushed Teeth		
Combed Hair		
Clothes Changed		
Other:		